PLAY DRUMS
BOB MARLEY

Wise Publications
part of The Music Sales Group

London / New York / Paris / Sydney / Copenhagen / Berlin / Madrid / Hong Kong / Tokyo

DRUM KIT NOTATION KEY

The following system of drum kit notation is employed in this book:

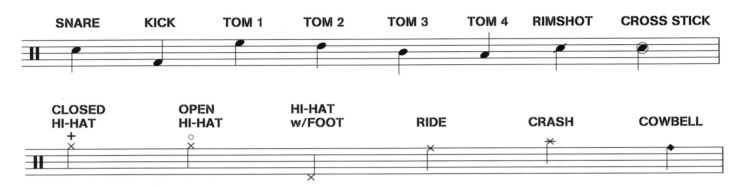

SNARE　　KICK　　TOM 1　　TOM 2　　TOM 3　　TOM 4　　RIMSHOT　　CROSS STICK

CLOSED HI-HAT　　OPEN HI-HAT　　HI-HAT w/FOOT　　RIDE　　CRASH　　COWBELL

Published by
Wise Publications
14-15 Berners Street, London W1T 3LJ, UK.

Exclusive Distributors:
Music Sales Limited
Distribution Centre, Newmarket Road,
Bury St Edmunds, Suffolk IP33 3YB, UK.
Music Sales Pty Limited
20 Resolution Drive,
Caringbah, NSW 2229, Australia.

Order No. AM1004124
ISBN 978-1-78038-377-4

Printed in the EU

www.musicsales.com

Edited by Adrian Hopkins
Cover designed by Liz Barrand

All Guitars: Arthur Dick
Bass Guitar: Paul Townsend
Drums: Noam Lederman
Keyboards: Paul Honey
Percussion: Fergus Gerrand
Trumpet: Edward Maxwell
Additional programming & Keyboards:
Rick Cardinali & Jonas Persson
Recorded and mixed by Jonas Persson

Your Guarantee of Quality
As publishers, we strive to produce every book
to the highest commercial standards.
The music has been freshly engraved and the book has
been carefully designed to minimise awkward page turns
and to make playing from it a real pleasure.
Particular care has been given to specifying acid-free,
neutral-sized paper made from pulps which have not been
elemental chlorine bleached. This pulp is from farmed
sustainable forests and was produced with special regard
for the environment.
Throughout, the printing and binding have been planned
to ensure a sturdy, attractive publication which should
give years of enjoyment.
If your copy fails to meet our high standards,
please inform us and we will gladly replace it.

CD TRACKS 1-8: FULL INSTRUMENTAL PERFORMANCES (WITH DRUMS)

CD TRACKS 9-16: BACKING TRACKS ONLY (WITHOUT DRUMS)

TO REMOVE THE CD FROM THE PLASTIC SLEEVE, LIFT THE SMALL LIP TO BREAK THE PERFORATION.
REPLACE THE DISC AFTER USE FOR CONVENIENT STORAGE.

Buffalo Soldier
(Marley/Williams) EMI Music Publishing Limited/
Campbell Connelly & Company Limited

Could You Be Loved
(Marley) Blue Mountain Music Limited

Exodus
(Marley) Blue Mountain Music Limited

Get Up, Stand Up
(Marley/Tosh) Blue Mountain Music Limited/
Campbell Connelly & Company Limited/
Chrysalis One Publishing UK Ltd

I Shot The Sheriff
(Marley) Blue Mountain Music Limited

Jamming
(Marley) Blue Mountain Music Limited

No Woman, No Cry
(Ford) Blue Mountain Music Limited

Waiting In Vain
(Marley) Blue Mountain Music Limited

BUFFALO SOLDIER

WORDS & MUSIC BY BOB MARLEY & NOEL WILLIAMS

FULL PERFORMANCE DEMO: TRACK 1
BACKING ONLY: TRACK 9

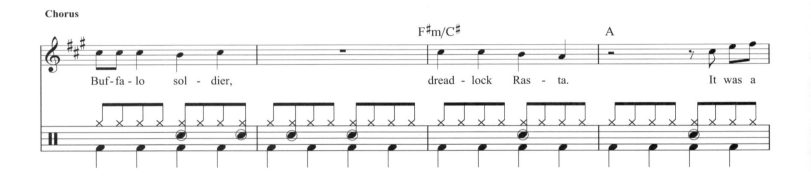

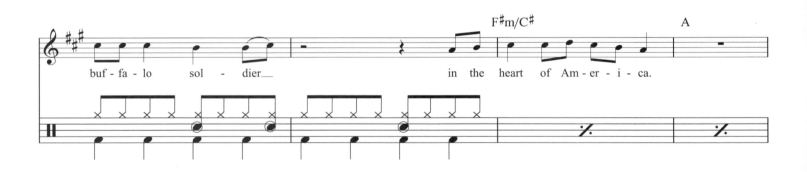

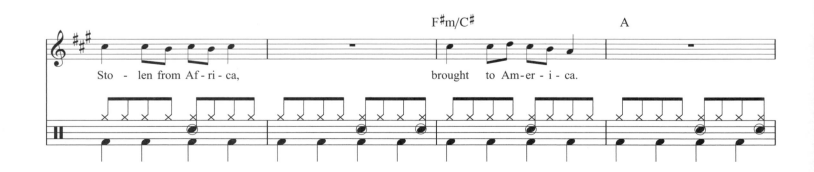

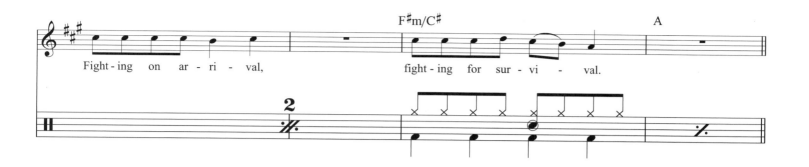

Fight - ing on ar - ri - val, fight - ing for sur - vi - val.

Verse

If you know your his - tor - y, then you would know where you're com-ing from.

Then you would-n't have to ask me,_ Who the heck do you think I am? I'm just a

Chorus

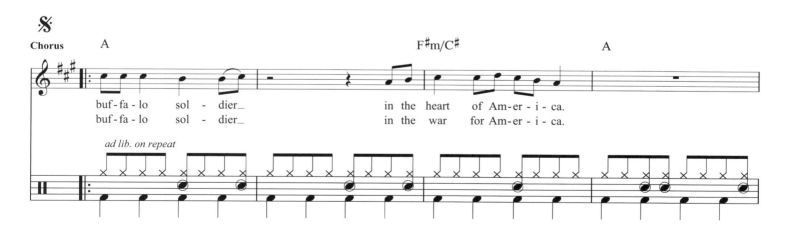

buf - fa - lo sol - dier_ in the heart of Am-er - i - ca.
buf - fa - lo sol - dier_ in the war for Am-er - i - ca.

ad lib. on repeat

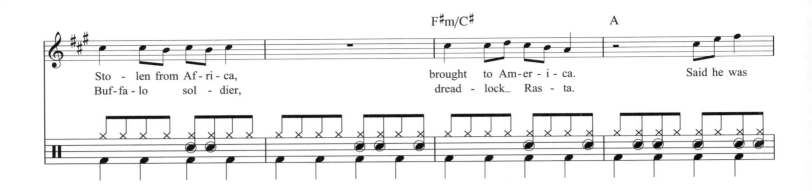

Sto - len from Af - ri - ca, brought to Am-er - i - ca. Said he was
Buf-fa - lo sol - dier, dread - lock_ Ras - ta.

fight-ing on ar - riv - al, fight-ing for sur - viv - al. Said he was a
Fight-ing on ar - riv - al, fight-ing for sur - viv - al.

To Coda

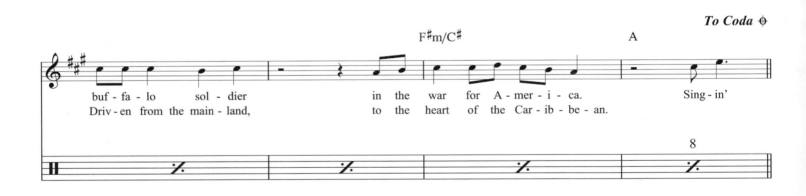

buf-fa - lo sol - dier in the war for A - mer - i - ca. Sing - in'
Driv - en from the main - land, to the heart of the Car - ib - be - an.

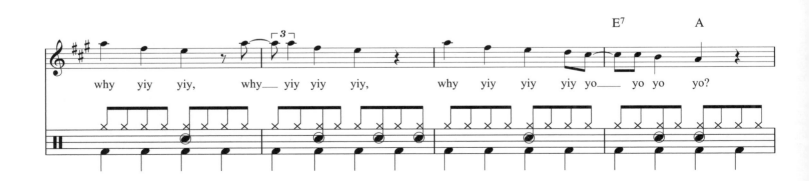

why yiy yiy, why__ yiy yiy yiy, why yiy yiy yiy yo__ yo yo yo?

Bridge

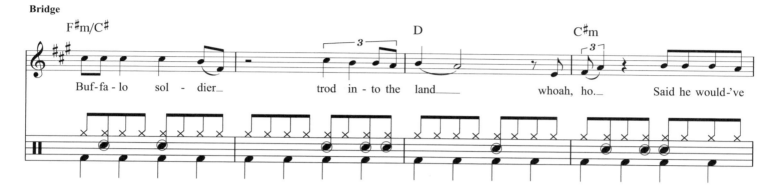

D.S. al Coda

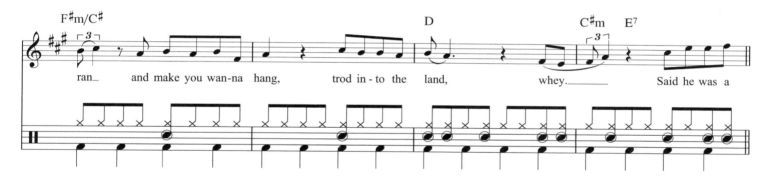

⊕ *Coda*

Repeat to fade

COULD YOU BE LOVED

WORDS & MUSIC BY BOB MARLEY

FULL PERFORMANCE DEMO: TRACK 2
BACKING ONLY: TRACK 10

♩ = 104

Intro
2 bar count in:

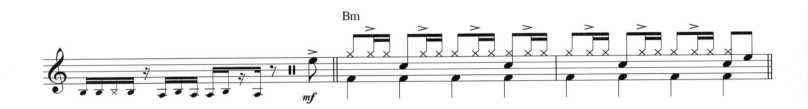

Chorus

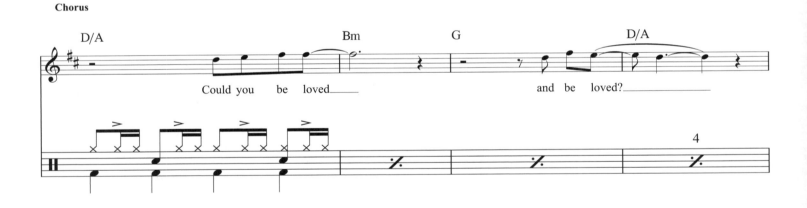

Could you   be   loved____   and   be   loved?____

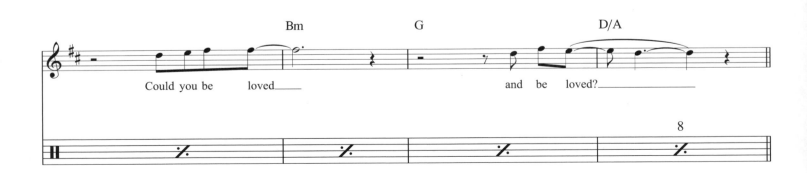

Could you be   loved____   and   be   loved?____

Bm   Em/B

1. Don't let   them fool_____ ya
2. Don't let   them change_____ ya,   ba-dum - pum - pi - dum, pum-pum-pum.   Sa-

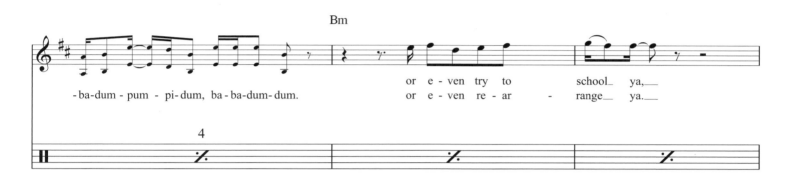

Bm

-ba-dum - pum - pi - dum, ba - ba-dum-dum.   or e - ven try to   school__ ya,__
                                             or e - ven re - ar - range__ ya.__

4

Em/B   Bm

oh,   no._____   We've   got
Oh,   no._____   We've   got

8

G   F#m   Em/B

a mind of our own.__   So, go to hell   if what you're think-ing is not right.__
the life to live.__   They say

12

I SHOT THE SHERIFF

WORDS & MUSIC BY BOB MARLEY

FULL PERFORMANCE DEMO: TRACK 4
BACKING ONLY: TRACK 12

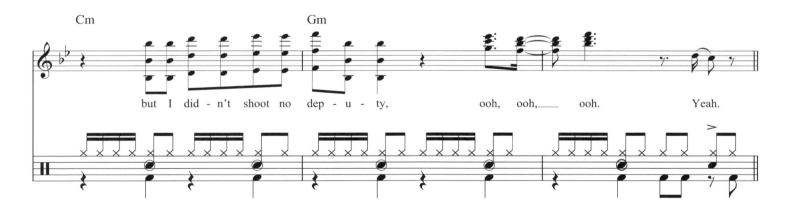

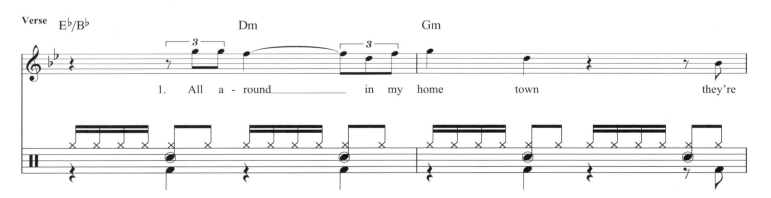

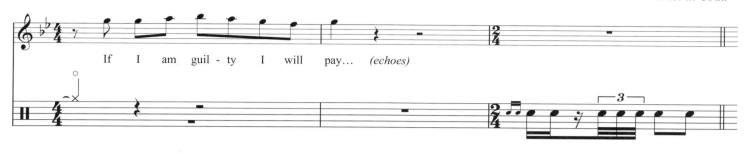

If I am guil-ty I will pay... *(echoes)*

✛ *Coda*

Straight

Outro Chorus

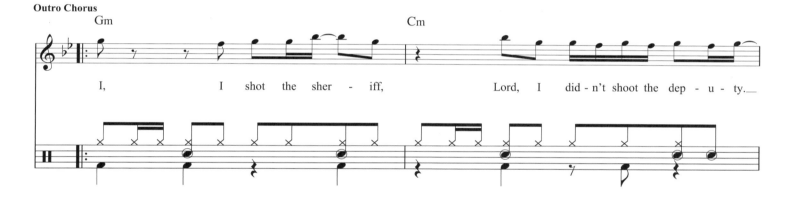

Gm   Cm

I,   I shot the sher-iff,   Lord, I did-n't shoot the dep-u-ty.___

Gm

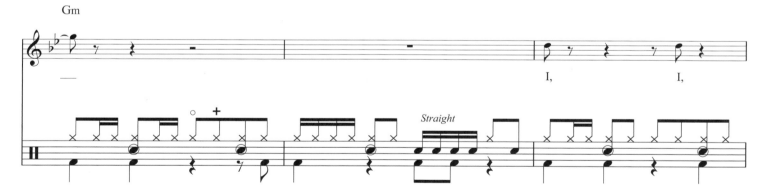

___   I,   I,

Straight

Cm   Gm   *repeat w/ad lib. vocals to fade*

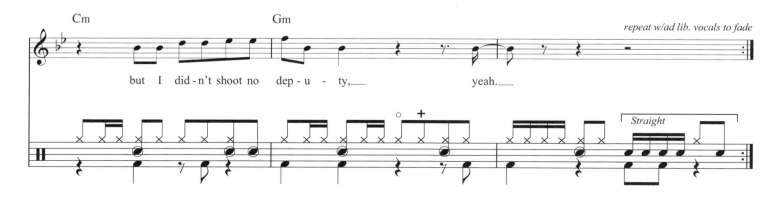

but I did-n't shoot no dep-u-ty,___   yeah.___

Straight

21

NO WOMAN, NO CRY

WORDS & MUSIC BY VINCENT FORD

FULL PERFORMANCE DEMO: TRACK 7
BACKING ONLY: TRACK 15

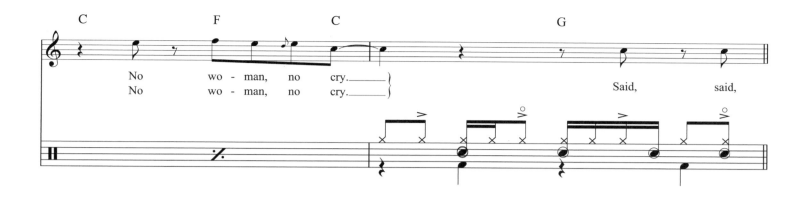

No wo - man, no cry.___

No wo - man, no cry.___

Said, said,

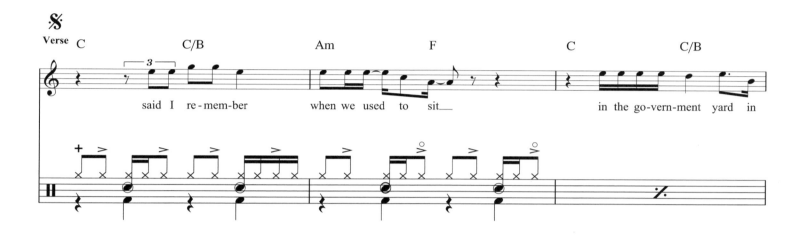

Verse

said I re - mem - ber when we used to sit___ in the go - vern - ment yard in

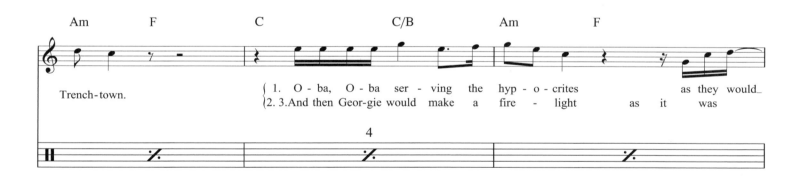

Trench - town.

1. O - ba, O - ba ser - ving the hyp - o - crites as they would_

2. 3. And then Geor - gie would make a fire - light as it was

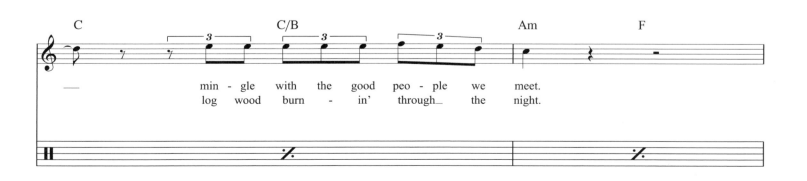

min - gle with the good peo - ple we meet.

log wood burn - in' through the night.

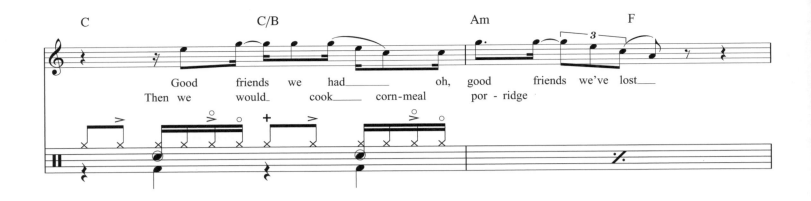

Good friends we had_____ oh, good friends we've lost_____
Then we would__ cook_____ corn-meal por - ridge

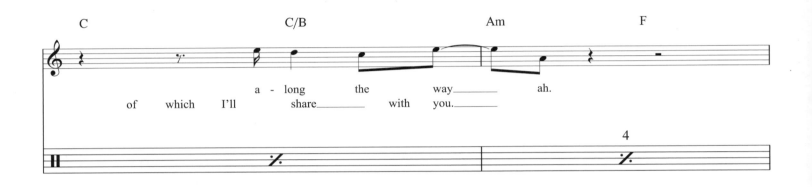

a - long the way_____ ah.
of which I'll share_____ with you._____

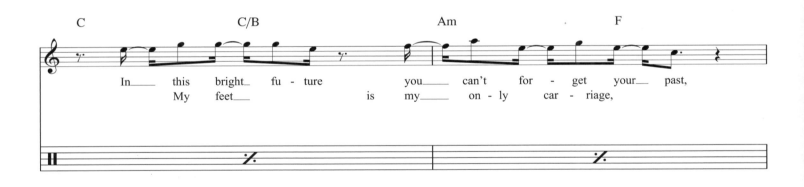

In_____ this bright__ fu - ture you_____ can't for - get your__ past,
My feet____ is my_____ on - ly car - riage,

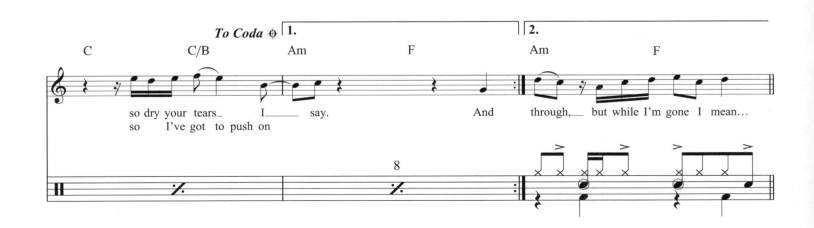

so dry your tears___ I_____ say.
so I've got to push on

And through,__ but while I'm gone I mean...

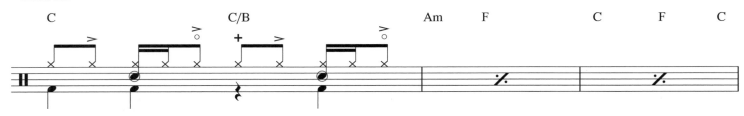

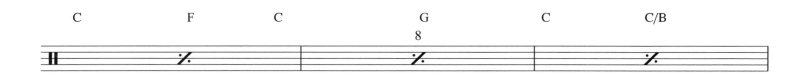

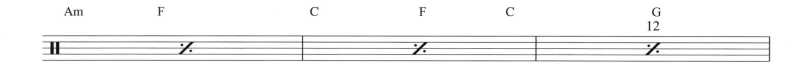

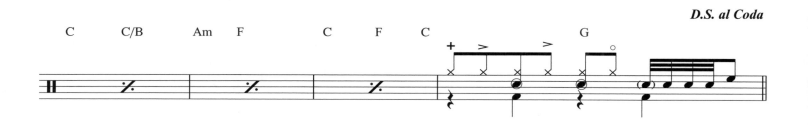

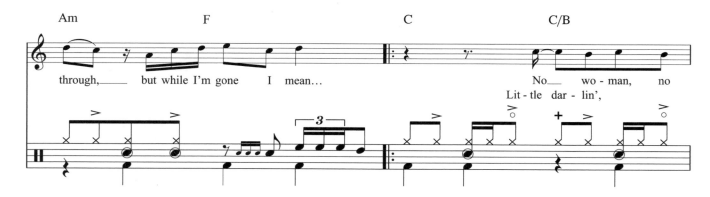

through,_____ but while I'm gone   I   mean...

No___ wo - man, no
Lit - tle dar - lin',

WAITING IN VAIN

WORDS & MUSIC BY BOB MARLEY

FULL PERFORMANCE DEMO: TRACK 8
BACKING ONLY: TRACK 16

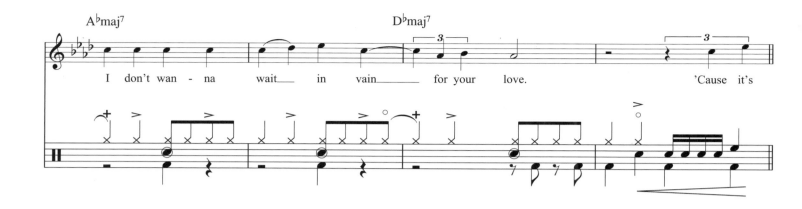

I don't wan - na wait__ in vain__ for your love. 'Cause it's

Bridge

sum - mer is here, I'm still wait - ing__ there.

Win - ter is here and I'm still wait - ing there.__

Guitar solo

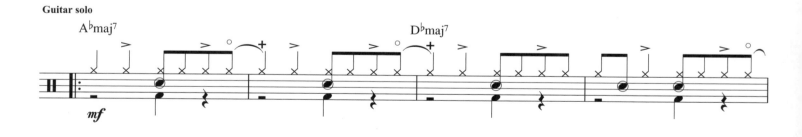

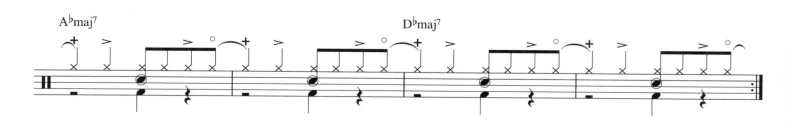

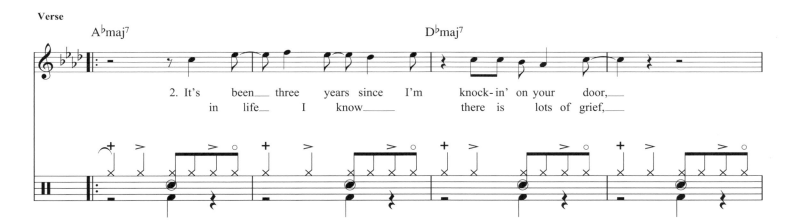

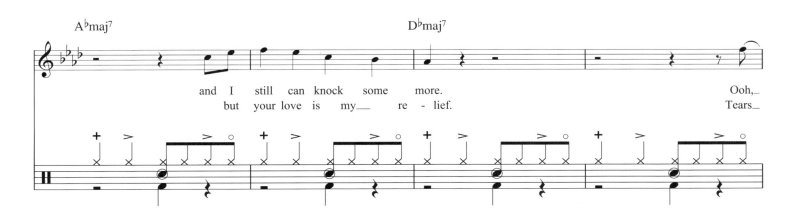

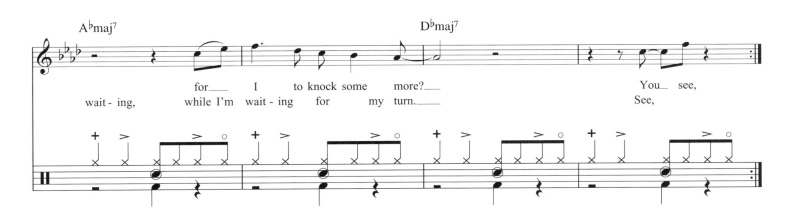